WHAT ON EARTH?

Desert

BART AND LYNN KING

High Noon Books
Novato, California

Editor: Michael Milone
Interior Illustrations: Cynthia Coverston
Cover Design: Bonni Gatter

International Standard Book Number: 978-1-57128-506-5

18 17 16 15 14 13 12 11 10 09
10 09 08 07 06 05 04 03 02 01

You will enjoy all the High Noon Books.
Write for a free full list of titles or visit us at
www.HighNoonBooks.com.

Contents

CHAPTER 1

Dry, Oh My!

Tess and Val quickly put up their tent. It had come with a list of steps. They followed each step. Sam and Nate had a hard time. They didn't want to read the list of steps. Then Nate started to boss Sam around. That did not help. Sam turned the whole thing into a joke.

Val's parents, Mr. and Mrs. Chase, had set up their tent. Her brother Max had a tent, too. His was a pup tent. Mrs. Chase opened two folding chairs and sat down. Mr. Chase joined her. He had changed his clothes. He was wearing colorful shorts and dark glasses. "Ahhh," he said. "This is the life!"

Val rolled her eyes at her father's funny shorts. She gave a look at Tess. "It's okay," said Tess. "My dad would do the same thing if he were here."

The Chases always took a trip the week after New Year's Day. Last year, it was New York. The year before, it was the coast of Maine. This year, they picked a place not far from home. It was less than a day's drive away.

Val and her three best pals had helped with the choice. They wanted their next film to be about the desert. Why not take a camping trip in the Southwest? It would be nice and warm. Plus, there would be so much to see and do. The Chases thought it was a great plan.

Tess had grabbed some printed handouts at the campground gate. They were full of facts about this desert. "Wow," said Tess. "It sure does get hot here! In the south part of this desert, it can be 134 degrees. That is in the shade!"

At this time of year it was nice and warm. It was about 70 degrees. At night, it cooled off a bit. On very cold nights, it got down to 32 degrees. "Who knew a desert could be so cold?" said Val.

"Some deserts are always cold," Tess said.

"Like the South Pole. It is an ice desert. It is also Earth's biggest desert."

This was news to Val. She thought all deserts were hot places with sand, not ice. How could a place like the South Pole be a desert? Tess said that it had to do with rain. A desert was a place with very little or no rain. In fact, some deserts went for years without a drop. It almost never rains or snows at the South Pole. That is why it is called a desert.

The girls sat on a flat rock. They studied the handout some more. This desert got less than three inches of rain a year! Could plants and animals live in such a place? They looked around. The campground was brown with dust.

There were few plants around. Had they made the right choice for their next film? Would they find much life in this dry desert?

Just then they heard a voice. "Oh, my!" it said.

It was a woman. She had set up camp at a site near theirs. The woman was bent over. Her white hair was tied into a bun. She was staring at the ground. Was she OK? Why was she talking to the ground?

The woman saw the girls. "Come, look," she said. "It's an ant lion trap!"

The ant lion is a bug. It makes a trap in the loose sand. The trap is a kind of hole. The ant lion hides in the sand. An ant might walk on the sand. It would get stuck. The ant lion would catch and eat the ant. That is what happened here. The ant lion had caught a meal.

"I wish I had my sketch book," said Val.

"Rule One," said the woman. "Do not go anywhere without your sketch book!" She pulled out a small pad and handed it to Val.

CHAPTER 2

Grand Land

The woman's name was Miss Jenn. She used to be a teacher. Now her job was drawing and painting. The thing she liked to paint best was the desert. "The land-forms here are so grand," she said.

Tess and Val brought Miss Jenn to meet the rest of their group. She sat with them and talked. She told them about some things they would see here.

There would be dunes. These were mounds

Tess and Val brought Miss Jenn to meet the rest of their group.

of loose sand. Some big deserts were just a sea of rolling dunes. This desert had a mix of landforms. There were a lot of rocks. Some of the rocks were huge and had odd shapes. They rose up from the desert floor. Other rocks were small. They filled the washes and dry stream beds.

"Hold on," said Nate. "I thought it did not rain much in the desert. Why are there stream beds here?"

Miss Jenn had been coming to this desert for years. She knew it well. She said that things in the desert could change fast. There might be no rain for weeks or months. Then there could be a short but heavy rain. The land was very hard and dry. The water could not soak into the ground. It moved fast over the land. It rushed to the dry stream beds. Water filled open places called draws. Sometimes there were flash floods. They happened quickly. Over time, the water cut a path through the land. It washed away sand and dirt. It left the rocks behind.

"Dry washes" were made this way. These were like small canyons or valleys. Canyons had steep rock walls. The group all knew about the Grand Canyon. It was about a mile deep and 277 miles long.

"What about those hills we saw from the car?" asked Sam. "The ones with flat tops and steep sides."

Miss Jenn said that the big ones were called mesas. "Mesa is the Spanish word for table. Can you see how they look like tables?" Miss Jenn asked. The small ones were called buttes. Miss Jean said the word like this: *byoots*. Water and wind helped to shape those, too. Loose rocks and sand had been washed away by rain. Wind blew sand and dirt away. What was left was a hill with a very flat top.

Val shook her head. "I don't get it. Why is this such a good place to draw and paint?"

Miss Jenn smiled. "You can't see much from this campground. It's just a place to sleep and to leave your stuff. A short hike from here is open desert. There are some great views.

11

There are vast plains of black rock. There are mesas and buttes that rise straight up. At sunset, they turn a deep rose. In the spring, this whole place is gold, red, and pink with blooms. There are many animals."

"And bugs!" said Nate. He pointed to the ground. Something red and fuzzy was marching past. "Is that two bugs?" he asked.

"Oh, my!" said Miss Jenn. "A velvet ant! It is just one bug. It looks like two because it has two main body parts."

Like the ant lion, the velvet ant is not an ant. The ant lion got its name because it eats ants. The velvet ant is a kind of wasp. It looks like a fuzzy ant. Val did not care if they were

12

ants or not. She liked all kinds of bugs. She

took out her pad to draw, and Miss Jenn smiled.

CHAPTER 3

Fun in the Sun

The next day, they met Miss Jenn for a hike. She had a spot where she liked to paint. Nate, Sam, Tess, Val, and Max would go with her. Then they would walk around and shoot some film. It would be more fun than staying back at the camp.

The sun was up, but no one could see it yet. Mountains in the east blocked the sun for now. The air was crisp. The ground was dry. It was dotted with rocks and dull gray-green plants.

14

The group hiked for a while. The sun came over the mountains. Even with the sun out, the land and plants seemed dull. This place lacked not just rain, but life. Now that they were in the desert, they were not sure about their choice. The desert was no place to make a film, they thought. It was too dry, dull, and dead!

Miss Jenn saw their sad faces. She made a quick change of plans. Today was not a day for her to paint. It was a day to teach about the desert.

She started with the desert plants. One by one, she pointed them out. The first one she told them about was a kind of small pine tree. Birds loved the seeds of the tree. The wood of this tree smelled good in a campfire.

Next, she showed them a cottonwood tree. In the spring, the tree has seeds. The seeds are in a kind of cotton. It blows all around. Long ago, folks named this tree "Pathfinder of the West." This was because the trees grew near streams. Folks thought the trees made a path to the water.

Now Miss Jenn talked about other plants. One was a smoke tree. The leaves of this tree are purple. Its blooms are like puffs of smoke! She said the desert paintbrush grew nearby. The blooms of this plant are bright red. They look as if they are dipped in paint. The cliff rose was a pretty bush. It had small white blooms and grew in rock walls. Folks made tea from its leaves. And here was a desert broom. The blooms of this bush turned into pods. In the hot sun, the pods burst. Seeds popped out and landed on the dry soil. With luck, they would start new broom plants. Long ago, folks used this plant to make brooms for sweeping.

Miss Jenn pinched a leaf from a gray-green plant. She broke the leaf into little bits. "Here, smell this," she said. The leaf had a strong but nice smell.

"Mmm," said Nate. "It smells like sage," he said.

"It is sage!" said Miss Jenn. "People have been cooking with this plant for ages. Bees love it, too. They make honey from its blooms."

Plant by plant, Miss Jenn made the desert come alive. This was not a dull place after all! One plant was called yellow beeplant. The blooms of this plant were used to make a black paint for clay pots. Another plant told the time. It was called the "desert four o'clock." This plant opened its flowers late in the afternoon.

Desert plants were strong. They grew in poor soil. They lived in a hot place with little water. Some plants stored water in their leaves, trunks and branches. Others sent their roots down deep.

The sun was low in the West when they headed back to camp. Bugs hummed and buzzed in the cooling air. Just then a bat zoomed past.

"Oh, my!" said Miss Jenn. "Have I told you about the bat caves?"

CHAPTER 4

Beat the Heat

There were caves in this desert! The caves were cool spots in a hot place. Animals stayed in them to beat the heat. Bats slept in the caves in the day. At night, the desert grew dark and cool. The bats flew out. They zipped around, catching bugs. In the morning, the bats went back to the caves.

The next day, Miss Jenn took the group to see the caves. On the way, Val thought she saw a dog.

"Look!" she said, pointing. "There, trotting along the base of that butte." The animal stopped for a bit. It looked at them. Then it kept going.

"That's a coyote," Miss Jenn said. She pronounced the word slowly. *Ky-OH-tee*.

"Is that the animal that howls like a dog?" asked Tess.

"Yes," said Miss Jenn. "Coyotes are part of the dog family. They live in packs. At night, they like to howl. People say it is the song of the desert."

"How about wolves?" asked Nate.

Miss Jenn said that she had not seen a wolf yet. They lived too far south of here. There

21

Coyotes are part of the dog family.

were also red and gray foxes in the desert.

It was about 5:00 PM when they reached the cave. The sky was getting dark. A few bats were flying from the cave. They dipped and dived this way and that.

Just then, something big swooped down. Its wings were about three feet across. It grabbed one of the bats and flew off.

"What was that?" asked Sam.

"It might have been a hawk," said Miss Jenn. "Or maybe it was an owl. Both the red-tail hawk and the great horned owl eat bats. Did anyone see its head? A hawk has a small head. An owl has a bigger head."

They were not sure what they had seen. If

only they had caught it on film. Then they could

have gone back and watched the scene again.

CHAPTER 5

Name Game

"Ouch!" said Sam. "Stay away from that plant. It hurts!"

Sam was talking about a cactus. These plants had spines. Some had spines that were big and long. They looked like pins. You knew not to touch them. Some had spines that were small. They looked like fuzz. Cactus fuzz was not soft, though. It was sharp.

Cactus comes in all shapes and sizes. There are small round ones that looked like balls.

There are tall thick ones. Some look like they had arms that reached up to the sky. Sometimes a cactus got its name from how it looked.

Miss Jenn taught Tess, Val, Sam, Nate, and Max a name game. She told them the name of a cactus plant. Then they had to guess how the plant got that name. One plant was the pancake prickly pear. It looked like it was made of green pancakes. The flat green disks grew this way and that. They were dotted with long, sharp spines. The buckhorn cactus looked like its name, too. Its branches were like the horns of a deer. Then there was the fishhook cactus. Its spines were curved like fishing hooks.

Sam was in no mood to play games today.

Sometimes a cactus got its name from how it looked.

He had lost his key chain.

"Cheer up, Sam," said Tess. "I'm sure it will turn up."

"It was right there beside the tent with my stuff," said Sam. "Where could it have gone?"

Nate told Sam to think back. "When was the last time you had it?" he asked.

Val made a joke. "I blame the roadrunner. He looks like a thief," she said. In truth, Val thought the roadrunner was sweet.

The roadrunner is a bird. Roadrunners can fly. But they like to walk and run on the ground. This one was about two feet long. Half of that was the bird's tail. Its body was mostly brown, with black and white streaks. A tall crest stood up from its head like a funny haircut. A patch of bright skin was next to each of its eyes.

The roadrunner was fast. It was named for how it runs along a road. This bird can go about 15 miles per hour!

At first, the group thought that the bird wanted something to eat. It showed up each time they sat down to have a meal. Miss Jenn told them no, that was not true. Roadrunners were just very friendly birds. They were not afraid of people. Roadrunners were not like another ground bird called the quail. These little round birds always ran away when they saw people.

The roadrunners seemed both brave and

bold. They were good at feeding themselves, too. They ate bugs, mice, and lizards. One time, Miss Jenn had seen a roadrunner eat a snake! The snake was too big to eat all at once. So the bird just ate it bit by bit. "That snake hung out of the bird's mouth for hours!" said Miss Jenn.

One day, they heard a bird with a loud and pretty song. It was the desert thrasher. The thrasher was like the roadrunner. It was a ground bird. With its curved beak, it caught bugs and worms. It turned over leaves and twigs on the desert floor. It found fat grubs to eat.

Miss Jenn said there were more than 500 kinds of birds in the desert. They had seen and heard lots of them. Still, there was one bird they talked about most of all. It was the hunting bird they had seen at the bat caves. What kind of bird was it? They set out to look for clues.

CHAPTER 6

Whoo Hoo!

It was hot by then. The sun was high in the sky. Nate took a long drink of water. He shook his head. "I don't know how they do it," he said.

"Who?" asked Val. "My folks? They love camping."

"No," said Nate with a laugh. "Not your folks. The desert animals." He shrugged. "The only water here is what we brought from home!"

"Miss Jenn said that desert plants can store

water," said Tess. "We can't see it, but it is there. The water is in the leaves, stems, trunks, and roots. Animals eat these plants and roots. They get water that way."

"They get it from eating bugs and other animals, too," said Val.

Sam had to tell them what he knew. "Camels store water in their humps!" he said.

All of them looked at Sam. They had to smile. Camels did not live in this desert! And camels stored fat in their humps, not water.

Tess knew some cool facts about camels. She said that camels lived in other deserts. They ate plants. Some of these deserts had few plants. The fat in the camels' humps helped them stay alive when food was hard to find. If a camel had no food, its hump grew small. Sometimes the hump became a slump. It slipped off the camel's back. The hump hung down on its side! Once a camel started to eat, the hump grew fat again.

Val spotted a lizard on the sand. It was doing an odd dance. It kept lifting one foot and then the other.

The five of them got as close as they could. Nate shot some film. They made sure not to scare the lizard. Its body was smooth, with scales that matched the ground. It had an odd short tail. What kind of lizard was this? They would ask Miss Jenn when they got back to the campground.

They hiked on. At last, they reached the bat caves. They looked around. There were no bats this time of day. There were no hunting birds around. The group looked for clues about the bird they had seen the other night. They found nothing. All they knew was that the bird had flown south.

Going south, they found a cliff wall. The wall was steep and rocky. They stood at the base of the cliff and looked up. They knew that hawks and owls might nest here. They saw nothing. They still did not know what kind of bird had caught the bat.

"Look at this," said Tess. She held a feather in her hand. It was just the clue they needed.

The feather was not from a hawk. It was from an owl. The bird that caught the bat was a great horned owl.

That night they sat around the campfire. They showed the feather to Miss Jenn. Just then, they heard a sound. It came from far away in the south. "Whoo! Hoo-hoo!"

"This feather is from a great horned owl," said Miss Jenn. "And so is that sound." She said she had a hunch it was a great horned owl. "A family of owls has lived here for years."

Then they told her about the lizard. She laughed. "Lots of lizards dance that way. The sand gets too hot. They lift their feet to cool them off! Did you see it run?" she asked. "It may have been a whiptail. They run fast, up on their hind legs."

Nate told her they had not seen it run. Its tail was short, though. It was nothing like a whip.

"Oh," said Miss Jenn. "Your lizard was growing a new tail!" She told them how she knew this.

Lizards sometimes lost their tails. They did it to save their lives. A bird or snake might grab a lizard by the tail. The tail would break off, but keep moving. The tail will seem like a worm. The bird or snake will look at the tail. The lizard can get away.

"Hey!" Sam called from his tent. "Has

anyone seen my pen light? It's gone just like my key chain! I put both of them right beside the opening of the tent."

CHAPTER 7

Packing and Tracking

It was their last day in the desert. Val and Tess were taking down the tents. Nate, Sam, and Max were cleaning up the campsite. Mr. and Mrs. Chase were putting things in the car.

"If you find any of my missing stuff, let me know!" Sam told the girls.

"Hey, everybody" said Nate. "Check this out!" Nate pointed to some prints on the ground. They were paw prints. Each print had four round toes and a round pad. The prints went around their campsite and out to the desert.

They went and got Miss Jenn. "I think these are cat tracks," she said. "I'm not sure what kind of cat." The tracks were too small for a mountain lion. Those cats had huge paws. Could these be bobcat tracks?

"What does a bobcat look like?" Val wanted to know.

Miss Jenn showed them a drawing she had made of a bobcat. A bobcat is bigger than a house cat. It has a short tail and pointed ears. Val saw long puffs of fur growing from each side of its face. Miss Jenn had drawn the fur on its body tan with spots. She said a grown bobcat weighed between 15 and 30 pounds.

A bobcat is bigger than a house cat. It has a short tail and pointed ears.

There was time for one last hike. Miss Jenn went with them. They wanted to see where these cat tracks led. Maybe the cat had been looking for food. Wild cats hunt at night. They like to be alone. Most of the time, they stay away from places with people.

"What do bobcats eat?" asked Nate as they walked.

"Mostly rabbits," said Miss Jenn. "But they also eat birds and mice."

"Not snakes?" asked Sam. He picked up a long piece of snake skin from the ground.

Miss Jenn smiled. "Sometimes they eat snakes. But our bobcat did not leave that skin. A snake shed that skin. As snakes grow, they drop off their old skin. A new skin takes its place."

The tracks took them off the path. They led to a clump of plants. The plants had tall spiked leaves. Miss Jenn said they were yucca plants. There were many kinds of yucca in the desert. Rope was made from its leaves. Soap could be made from its roots.

Under the clump of yuccas, there was something odd. "What are all the sticks for?" asked Val. "It looks like some kind of nest!"

"The tracks have led us to a wood rat's nest! The cat was probably hunting the wood rats," said Miss Jenn. "Wood rats have big ears and hairy tails. They pick up things that catch their eye. They bring the stuff back to their nest. That is why we sometimes call them pack rats!" This wood rat had odd things in its nest. Mixed in with the sticks, they saw all kinds of stuff. There was a spoon and a pink thumbtack.

"Look," said Val. "It's Sam's key chain and pen light! A wood rat must have come by the tents when we were asleep. Maybe it borrowed the key chain and pen light."

Everyone laughed at Val's idea. Sam said, "I hope the wood rat asks me before it borrows anything else."